HAND-ARM VIBRATION

HS(G)88

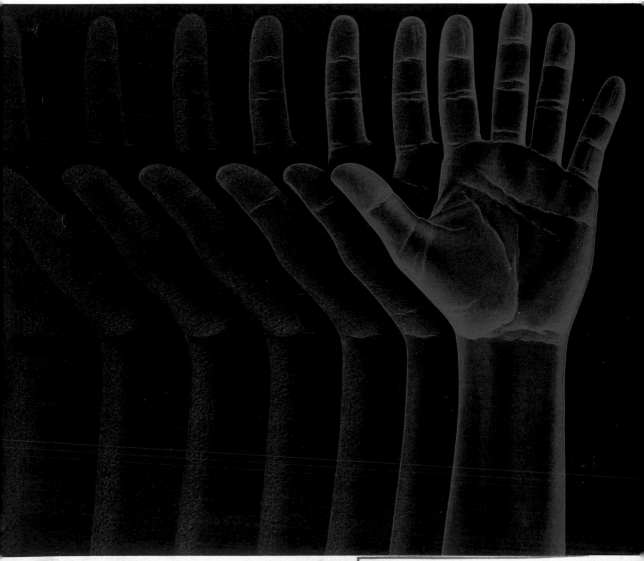

HSE BOOKS

© Crown copyright 1994
Applications for reproduction should be made to HMSO
First published 1994

ISBN 0 7176 0743 7

HS(G) Series

The purpose of this series is to provide guidance for those who have duties under the Health and Safety at Work etc Act 1974 and other relevant legislation. It gives guidance on the practical application of legislation, but it should not be regarded as an authoritative interpretation of the law.

CONTENTS

FOREWORD

Over the last few years there has been growing concern about the need to reduce the effect that prolonged and regular work with high-vibration hand-held tools can have on the hands and arms of users. Without effective controls, workers using such equipment may suffer various forms of damage, collectively known as 'hand-arm vibration syndrome' (HAVS). The best known form of damage is 'vibration white finger' (VWF), which is a prescribed industrial disease.

There are no specific legal duties or measures which must be taken to reduce the risk of HAVS. However, if workers are at risk, employers, employees and machine makers need to consider what action is necessary to reduce the risk so far as is reasonably practicable to meet the requirements of general legislation, including the Health and Safety at Work etc Act 1974 (HSW Act) and the Management of Health and Safety at Work Regulations 1992. Applying the advice given in this guidance should, in HSE's view, ensure that the risks from HAVS are properly controlled.

The first chapter of the guidance is intended to help managers and others decide where there might be a risk and what kind of programme might help to reduce it. The remaining chapters give technical advice for specialist staff to implement any necessary programmes. Some of the recommendations may not be appropriate for all jobs or machines, so they might need to be adapted for local circumstances. However, they should provide a basis for the development of programmes suited to the great majority of situations where hand-arm vibration creates hazards.

This guidance explains the difficulties, with present technology, of accurately assessing vibration exposure. These problems can make it difficult to decide whether workers doing some jobs should be included in a health surveillance programme. It is important, therefore, that those who are not included in any such programme are given full information about the risks and signs of injury. They should be encouraged to report any such signs so that they can be further assessed by an occupational physician or nurse, and so that management can consider measures to improve control, including reducing exposure and extending the health surveillance programme.

This guidance is intended to be a framework document and source of reference for use by all those involved in identifying and controlling the risks of HAVS and is therefore fairly comprehensive. For those requiring a simpler introduction to the hazard and a brief summary of what can be done about it, free leaflets are available. See the 'Further reading' section at the end of the book for more details.

CHAPTER ONE

KEY POINTS

■ Hand-arm vibration syndrome (HAVS) is a widespread industrial disease affecting tens of thousands of workers. Its best known effect is vibration-induced white finger (VWF).

■ Attacks are painful and can result in the loss of the ability to grip properly.

■ Any vibrating tool or process which causes tingling or numbness after 5 to 10 minutes of continuous use is suspect.

■ Tools and processes likely to be hazardous are listed in the guidance. Where people regularly work with these for prolonged periods there is likely to be a risk of injury. Sometimes it is possible to assess the danger by measuring the vibration exposure, but with current technology this is often difficult or impractical.

■ Preventive programmes can do much to control the risk. Such programmes include:

  ■ identifying hazardous jobs;

  ■ vibration control;

  ■ information and training for workers and their supervisors;

  ■ routine health surveillance.

■ Machine makers and suppliers should take vibration into account when designing products and information packages.

INTRODUCTION

1   Workers whose hands are regularly exposed to high vibration may suffer from several kinds of injury to the hands and arm, including impaired blood circulation and damage to the nerves and muscles. Collectively the injuries are known as 'hand-arm vibration syndrome' (HAVS), though other names are sometimes used in industry, including 'dead finger', 'dead hand' or 'white finger'. This is a painful disease and is widespread in those industries where vibratory tools and machines are used.

INJURIES CAUSED BY HAND-ARM VIBRATION

2   Hand-arm vibration syndrome is a general term embracing various kinds of damage, including:

■   vascular disorders generally known as 'vibration-induced white finger' (VWF) causing impaired blood circulation and blanching of affected fingers and parts of the hand;

■   neurological and muscular damage leading to numbness and tingling in the fingers and hands, reduced grip strength and dexterity, and reduced sensitivity both of touch and to temperature;

■   other possible kinds of damage leading to pain and stiffness in the hands and joints of the wrists, elbows and shoulders. These forms

of damage and the factors contributing to them are less well understood than the vascular and neurological effects.

3   In the first stages of vibration injury, the worker may notice a tingling sensation or 'pins and needles' in the fingers. This is most noticeable at the end of a working day and may be accompanied by numbness. With continued exposure, the person may suffer periodic attacks in which the fingers change colour when exposed to the cold. In mild cases, the whiteness and numbness only affect the tips of the fingers. As the condition becomes more severe, the whole finger down to the knuckles becomes white.

4   At first a typical attack might occur when the sufferer leaves for work on a cold winter morning and notices that the fingers rapidly become pale and feeling is lost. This phase is followed by an intense red flush (sometimes preceded by a dusky bluish phase) signalling the return of blood circulation to the fingers and is usually accompanied by uncomfortable throbbing.

5   In more severe forms, attacks occur frequently in cold weather. They are likely to take place not only at work, but during activities such as gardening, car washing, fishing, or watching outdoor sports. The attacks may last up to an hour, causing considerable pain and loss of manual dexterity, resulting in clumsiness and reduced grip strength. As the condition worsens, attacks can occur even in warm surroundings.

6   In very severe cases, blood circulation may be permanently impaired and fingers may take on a blue-black appearance. Exceptionally, gangrene may result. However, it is very rare for these stages to be reached because the earlier symptoms cause most sufferers to abandon work using high-vibration equipment.

7   The first noticeable symptoms may occur some time after regular exposure to vibration has begun. In the early stages, improvement may occur when the worker gives up activities associated with vibration. Later, however, the condition is likely to become permanent.

8   Where VWF is contracted by workers who are involved in certain specific work activities, it is reportable under the Reporting of Injuries, Diseases and Dangerous Occurrences Regulations 1985 (RIDDOR).[1] VWF is also a prescribed disease and Industrial Injuries Disablement Benefit may be payable by the Department of Social Security.*

9   Various schemes are commonly used for grading the severity of the injury. For industrial health surveillance, the system described as 'Stockholm Workshop' is recommended. This and other common systems used in the United Kingdom are discussed in Chapter 3.

FACTORS CONTRIBUTING TO RISK

10   The primary cause of HAVS is work which involves holding vibrating tools or workpieces. Vibration with a frequency ranging from about 2 to 1500 Hertz (cycles per second or Hz) is potentially damaging, and is most hazardous in the range from about 5 to 20 Hz. The risk depends on both the vibration magnitude and how long people are exposed to it, in effect a daily 'vibration dose', as described in paragraph 18.

11 Several other factors also affect the severity of the risk, although there is still only limited scientific information on their importance and the way they interact. These include:

■   the grip, push and other forces used to guide and apply vibrating tools or workpieces. A tight grip transfers more vibration energy to the hand;

■   the exposure pattern - length and frequency of work and rest periods. It is better to break up periods of exposure;

■   how much of the hand is exposed to vibration;

■   factors affecting blood circulation, such as temperature and smoking;

■   individual susceptibility.

* Information on Industrial Injuries Disablement Benefit is given in the free Department of Social Security leaflet NI 2 *If you have an industrial disease*, published by the Benefits Agency.

IDENTIFYING HAZARDOUS WORK AND ASSESSING RISK

12 Common tools and processes likely to create hazardous vibration are listed in this paragraph. They will not always cause injury because the risk also depends on the frequency of use, the way the tools are designed and used, and the working conditions. Nevertheless, the possibility of risk should be investigated where they are regularly used for prolonged periods.

■ **Percussive metal-working tools**

Powered percussive metal-working tools, including powered hammers for riveting, caulking, hammering, clinching and flanging. Hammer swaging.

■ **Percussive tools used in stoneworking, quarrying, construction etc**

Percussive hammers, vibratory compactors, concrete breakers, pokers, sanders and drills used in mining, quarrying, demolition and road construction etc.

■ **Grinders and other rotary tools**

Pedestal grinders, hand-held portable grinders, flex-driven grinders and polishers, and rotary burring tools.

■ **Timber and wood machining tools**

Chain-saws, brush cutters (clearing saws), hand-held or hand-fed circular saws, electrical screwdrivers, mowers and shears, hardwood cutting machines, barking machines and strimmers.

■ **Other processes and tools**

Pounding machines used in shoe manufacture, drain suction machines, nut runners, concrete vibro-thickeners, and concrete levelling vibro-tables.

13 The list in paragraph 12 is not comprehensive. It is safest to regard regular prolonged use of any high-vibration tool or machine as suspect, especially if it causes tingling or numbness in the user's fingers after about 5 to 10 minutes continuous operation. Also, where any vibrating equipment is regularly used, employers should remain alert for symptoms among the workers which, once reported, should be investigated by someone able to assess them. If this indicates that injury is being caused, preventive and health surveillance programmes will probably be needed.

14 Where hazardous jobs are identified they should be taken into account in the general risk assessment required by the Management of Health and Safety at Work Regulations 1992. An Approved Code of Practice[2] gives guidance on the requirements of these Regulations.

15 It is sometimes possible to make a more accurate assessment by measuring exposure levels or calculating them from vibration data provided by machine makers. This can then be compared with the action level of exposure recommended in paragraph 21. However, in the present state of technology, reliable and accurate measurement of industrial exposures may often be difficult or impracticable and specialised skills are needed to carry them out. It will often be better to develop programmes from assessments of what is known about the hazard created by the kinds of tool used.

Vibration measurements and vibration exposure

16 Various methods have been developed to measure vibration, giving the results as the displacement, velocity or acceleration of vibrating surfaces.

17 Hazard to health is usually assessed from the average (root-mean-square, or rms) acceleration level, using an instrument with a standard 'frequency weighting network' or filter to reduce its sensitivity at the less damaging high and low frequencies. This gives the 'frequency-weighted acceleration' ($a_{h,w}$) in m/s^2. British Standard BS 6842:1987[3] describes a procedure for making these measurements.

18 The vibration 'dose' received by the worker over a typical working day depends on the duration of exposure as well as the vibration magnitude. To allow different exposure patterns to be compared, they are adjusted or 'normalised' to a standard reference period of 8 hours, however long the actual exposure period. The British Standard describes how an exposure normalised to 8 hours (A(8)) can be calculated. Other reference periods are sometimes used, notably that in

International Standard ISO 5349:1989[4] which uses a 4 hour base (to give exposure as A(4)). When comparing exposures it is important to make sure that the same reference periods are used.

19 If the machine maker can provide enough data on vibration levels under standard conditions it might be possible to calculate exposure from this data and from local information on how long workers will use the tools. This avoids the practical difficulties of measuring vibration, though care is needed to make sure that the vibration data are reasonably representative of what is likely when the tools are being used for the jobs being assessed. Chapter 4 contains a nomogram to help make these calculations. It is good practice to ask for vibration data before deciding which new machines to buy.

20 Chapter 4 also gives more technical advice on how measurements can be made and levels of A(8) calculated from them. With the instruments available today, hand-arm vibration measurement is not simple and should be carried out by someone with adequate competence.

21 Programmes of preventive measures and health surveillance are recommended where workers' exposure regularly exceeds an A(8) of 2.8 m/s^2.* If a 4 hour normalising period is used this corresponds to an A(4) of 4 m/s^2. Table 1 gives average values of vibration over other working periods which are equivalent to an A(8) of 2.8 m/s^2.

---

* BS 6842:1987 indicates that there is some evidence suggesting that exposure at this level may cause finger blanching in about 10% of the vibration-exposed population after 8 years. This estimate is subject to considerable uncertainty. The action level should not therefore be regarded as a completely 'safe' level.

Table 1 *Average vibration levels over the working day which cause an A(8) of 2.8 m/s²*

Length of working day (hours)	16	8	4	2	1	½
rms average vibration level over working day (m/s²) to give A(8) of 2.8 m/s²)	2	2.8	4	5.6	8	11.2

PREVENTIVE PROGRAMME

22 A preventive programme should control the risk of injury if introduced where there is regular prolonged use of tools likely to be hazardous, or where it is known that vibration exposure will exceed the 'action level' in paragraph 21.

Training and information

23 Train and provide information for workers and their supervisors on:

■ the nature of the risk, and signs of injury;

■ how and why any signs of injury should be reported, either to someone who will arrange for them to be investigated, or as part of an established routine health survelllance programme;

■ action the workers should take to minimise risk, including:

■ using working practices designed to minimise vibration being directed into the hands;

■ maintaining good blood circulation;

■ making sure tools are properly maintained;

■ reporting defects and problems with equipment and obtaining replacements where necessary.

Vibration control

24 Vibration energy directed into the worker's hands should be reduced so far as is reasonably practicable.* Measures to achieve this include:

■ substituting a process involving less vibration, for example by replacing hammer swaging with roller pointing;

■ using tools designed for low vibration, for example chain-saws with anti-vibration mountings and tools with vibration-isolating handles;

* As well as the general duties under the HSW Act, the Provision and Use of Work Equipment Regulations 1992 require that employers select and use equipment that is suited to maintain the health and safety of the user. See *Work Equipment. Provision and Use of Work Equipment Regulations 1992. Guidance on Regulations* L22 HSE 1992 ISBN 0 7176 0414 4.

- correct and routine maintenance of tools;

- arrangements to reduce the grip, push and other forces which the worker must apply, for example supports for tools and workpieces, and good ergonomic design of processes and equipment;

- using tools designed to avoid the need for workers to grip high-vibration parts such as a chisel fitted into a chipping hammer;

- training workers in operating techniques which minimise the need to grip tools and workpieces tightly;

- avoiding uninterrupted vibration exposure over long periods. It is better for work to be arranged so that periods of exposure are broken by periods of work which do not involve vibration;

- proper selection of tools for the task.

25   Various sorts of gloves with special soft linings intended to provide vibration-isolation are commercially available, but they are not usually effective in reducing the amount of vibration reaching the worker's hands. The amount of vibration reduction they can give is limited by practical restrictions on the thickness and softness of the lining, particularly at low frequencies. They will usually provide little or no protection against vibration at the most damaging frequencies, and poorly selected gloves might even increase the vibration transmitted to the wearer's hands.* However, gloves are useful for their ability to keep hands warm and provide physical protection.

Maintaining blood circulation

26   Keeping the hands and body warm helps to maintain good blood flow to the fingers and reduce the risk of injury. Where people have to work in cold areas, specific measures might include:

- wearing gloves;

- using proprietary heating pads to keep the hands warm;

- using tools with heated handles;

- avoiding pneumatic exhausts which discharge towards the worker's hands (a flexible hose to lead the exhaust away might also help with noise control);

- arrangements to allow workers to warm up before starting work, and if necessary to help them keep warm, such as a shelter for outdoor workers to use in work breaks;

- wearing warm, weatherproof clothing for work in cold or wet areas.

27   Avoiding or cutting down smoking, and massaging and exercising fingers during work breaks will also help blood circulation.

* European standards makers (CEN Technical Committee TC 231/WG3) are (in 1994) preparing a standard on anti-vibration gloves.

HEALTH SURVEILLANCE PROGRAMME

28 The Management of Health and Safety at Work Regulations 1992 require employers to provide appropriate health surveillance for employees where the risk assessment shows it to be necessary. The associated Approved Code of Practice gives general guidance on the factors to be taken into account in deciding when it should be introduced.

29 For work involving hand-held or hand-guided vibratory tools, these factors indicate that health surveillance is likely to be appropriate for all workers in jobs identified as giving rise to significant risk of HAVS (see paragraphs 13 and 21). The surveillance programme should enable symptoms to be assessed and appropriate information to be given to individuals regarding further exposure to vibration.

30 The elements of a good programme include checking workers under the general supervision of a medical practitioner; a system for workers to report any episodes of finger blanching (which should be investigated); and an adequate record keeping system of both medical examinations and any episodes of finger blanching. Chapter 3 gives more detailed advice for health professionals responsible for the programme.

31 Workers who develop episodes of

HAVS should report them to those nominated to receive notifications of symptoms under the health surveillance programme. The employer will need to set up a suitable system for them to do so. This might include a system of reports directly to an occupational physician or nurse, for example where they are regular visitors to the workplace. In others a designated person, possibly a first aider with suitable training, might be nominated. The reports are not, on their own, grounds for making a diagnosis, but act as a trigger for further assessment by an occupational health professional.

MACHINERY SUPPLIERS AND PURCHASING NEW MACHINES

32 Designers, manufacturers, importers and suppliers have responsibilities under section 6 of the HSW Act to supply machines and equipment which, so far as reasonably practicable, are safe and without risks to health, and to supply information about safe use.*

33 If risk of injury to the end user is to be kept to a minimum, vibration control and good ergonomic design needs to be considered at all stages of design and development. The 2.8 m/s^2 A(8) action level for daily exposure should not be used as a target for this purpose because it will not eliminate risk. The aim should be to produce tools which generate

---

* The duties are outlined in a free HSE leaflet *Articles and substances used at work: the legal duties of designers, manufacturers, importers and suppliers and erectors and installers* (IND(G)1(L) rev).

vibration exposures lower than this where reasonably practicable.

34 Information on hazardous vibration can be passed to the purchaser and user in various ways, including warning labels fixed to the machine or tool, technical information in data sheets about the equipment, and in the operating and installation instructions.

35 European Community Directive 89/392/EEC, as amended, on the safety of new machinery,[*] was implemented into United Kingdom law by the Supply of Machinery (Safety) Regulations 1992.[†] The Regulations require machine suppliers to provide instructions giving the requirements for reducing vibration relating to installation and assembly. More particularly, suppliers must provide information on vibration levels if hand-held or hand-guided machinery is likely to subject workers to vibration ($a_{h,w}$) exceeding 2.5 m/s^2 (ie the vibration magnitude when the tool is operating, not the A(8) vibration 'dose' over the whole working day).

36 Buyers of potentially hazardous machines should ask for information on vibration levels and the vibration control built into the equipment when deciding on a purchase. Appendix 1 gives examples of enquiries that might be made.

---

[*] The Directive specifies that machinery must be designed and constructed so that risk from vibration is reduced to the lowest level taking account of technical progress. European CEN standards makers intend to publish standards that machine makers can use to help them demonstrate compliance with these requirements.

[†] The Supply of Machinery (Safety) Regulations 1992 (ISBN 0 11 025719 7). Information on these requirements can be obtained from the Department of Trade and Industry, Standards Policy Unit, 151 Buckingham Palace Road, London SW1W 9SS.

CHAPTER TWO

Technical ways to reduce vibration

KEY POINTS

- **The basic reduction methods are to:**

  - **eliminate the hazard;**

  - **substitute an alternative low-vibration process;**

  - **reduce the vibration generated;**

  - **minimise the forces needed to apply and control tools;**

- **minimise transmission of vibration to the hands;**

- **decrease exposure times.**

- **Vibration reduction should be considered at the process and product design stages, when selecting tools, and when individual work tasks and work stations are being designed or assessed.**

INTRODUCTION

37 This section gives practical advice to engineers on ways to reduce exposure of workers to hand-arm vibration.

A STRATEGY TO REDUCE VIBRATION

38 An effective strategy to reduce vibration exposure is best developed by:

- identifying the chief sources of vibration;

- ranking them in terms of their contribution to the hazard;

- identifying and evaluating potential solutions in terms of practicability and cost;

- establishing targets which can be realistically achieved;

- allocating priorities and establishing an 'action programme';

- defining management responsibilities and allocating adequate resources;

- implementing the programme;

- monitoring progress;

- evaluating the programme.

METHODS TO REDUCE EXPOSURE

39 The basic methods are to:

- eliminate the hazard by substituting other non-hazardous processes, for example automated or mechanised processes;

- reduce vibration by modifying the machinery or process;

- reduce vibration transmission in the path between the source of vibration and the handles or other surfaces gripped by workers' hands;

- minimise the forces needed to apply and control the tools;

- reduce the length of exposure, for example through job rotation.

Product design

40 Vibration is best dealt with at the design stage. Product designers should evaluate alternative designs to:

- avoid or minimise the need for operations and tools exposing workers to hazardous vibration;

- facilitate the use of low-vibration tools or processes;

- facilitate the optimum ergonomic design of work spaces and tasks.

41 Some of the measures which might be possible include:

■ using adhesive or welded joints in a fabricated product rather than riveted joints to avoid the use of pneumatic riveting hammers;

■ using finishes for building surfaces which avoid the use of scabbling tools to produce a decorative effect;

■ maximising the use of off-site prefabrication to produce components of higher quality by mechanised methods, thus reducing on site 'cutting and patching' to fit;

■ careful design of metal castings (including the selection of the most suitable material) to reduce the degree of hand finishing (fettling) required;

■ mechanisation or automation of the process.

Process design

42   Substitution of low-vibration processes can do much to restrict vibration exposures. Examples include:

■ using mobile road cutting machines and/or trenching machines for cable laying, water and mains repairs and similar work instead of portable road breakers (see Figure 1);

■ reducing the use of road drills to demolish reinforced concrete structures by the use of hydraulic crushing or nibbling techniques (see Figure 2). Large blocks can be fragmented by the use of hydraulic expanding devices inserted into pre-drilled holes.

43   In foundries, the amount of fettling needed is affected by the design and material; by the method of manufacture selected; and the skill with which it is carried out. The better the casting, the less the need for manual rectification and finishing. For example, a company manufacturing castings of up to 350 tonnes in a variety of steel alloys substituted a moulding process based on the use of cold setting phenolic resins, in place of the traditional green sand method. It gave better casting quality and greatly reduced the amount of fettling and rectification work.

44   Process improvement can also increase productivity. In the ship building industry, chipping hammers and portable grinders have been used to prepare the edges of plates, dress welds and to remove the welded brackets and stiffeners (fairing aids) traditionally used to support and align parts of ship structures during assembly. A new approach involved cutting out the plates more accurately to ensure a better fit, then using magnetic or vacuum clamps and hydraulic devices to align them (see Figure 3).

45   In another firm, electronic detectors improved their ability to locate leaks from buried pipelines, reducing the need for road breakers. The same firm achieved a further increase in productivity and a reduction in vibration exposure by adopting a 'no dig' strategy for the replacement of ageing, buried pipe systems. Instead they used techniques involving scraping out and relining in situ.

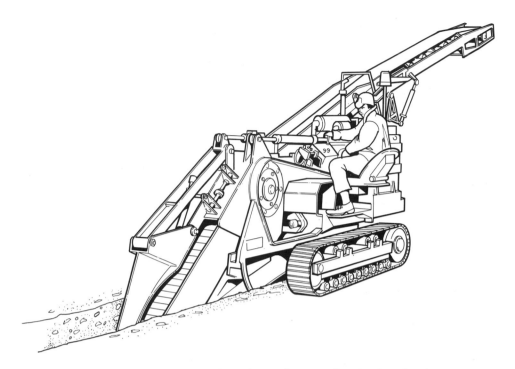

Figure 1   *Trenching machines can reduce the need to use vibrating hand tools*

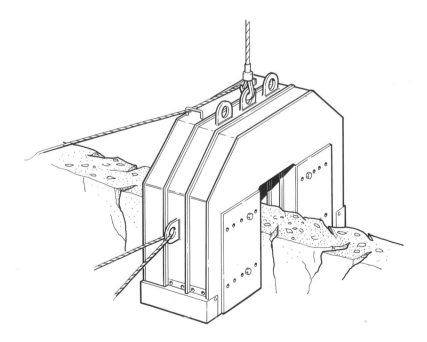

Figure 2   *Nibbling equipment to reduce the use of hand-held concrete breakers*

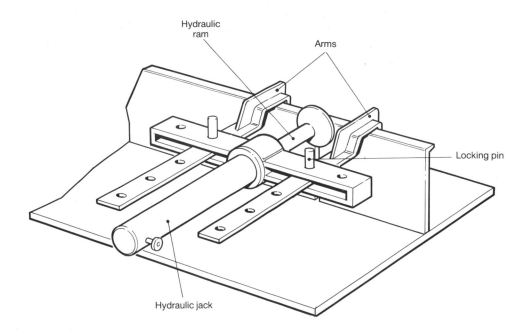

Figure 3 *Use of an hydraulic fairing aid to align butts before welding, avoiding the need for welded-on aids which must later be chipped away. (Sketch courtesy of Swan Hunter Shipbuilders Ltd)*

46 Some other methods to reduce vibration involve:

- using milling, turning or other machining operations in place of metal removing processes using powered hand tools. For example, when fettling castings, it can be more economic and less hazardous to rough machine, rather than hand fettle, surfaces which can later be machine finished;

- using Arc-air and other flame cutting or gouging methods instead of pneumatic chisels or portable grinders for the rough dressings of castings and similar work;

- using hydraulic rather than pneumatic impulsive riveting techniques;

- preliminary, chemical polishing processes to cut down on the need for polishing plated components.

Mechanisation

47 Mechanisation and remote control or automation can also help reduce exposure. For example, exposure from hand grinding precision components can be eliminated by automating the balancing process, improving the working environment and increasing productivity. In the foundry industry, productivity has been increased by using manipulators and remote control swing grinders allowing more power to be applied during fettling.

48 Other hazardous operations, such as those involving cut-off saws, for example when cleaning up castings, bar cutting and cutting concrete blocks and slabs, are improved or eliminated by the use of enclosed, remote-controlled or semi-automatic models (see Figure 4). This approach reduces vibration exposure, noise and dust and the physical effort required to perform the work.

49 Robots are being used increasingly in industry and various industrial organisations have developed robot or highly-automated grinders and burning machines for the removal of casting feeder heads and other fettling operations.

Equipment selection

50 Where hand-held or hand-guided tools are unavoidable, vibration exposure might be minimised by careful tool selection.

51 When purchasing equipment, ask suppliers to provide information about vibration magnitudes which their products are likely to create in normal use (see Appendix 1 for examples of enquiries which might be made). Where standards exist, draft a purchasing specification, incorporating maximum vibration magnitudes and test procedures, which suppliers have to satisfy.

52 Many manufacturers of hand-held or hand-guided machines now market one

or more low-vibration designs, for example for road drills, grinders, rammers, chipping hammers, sanders, or machines incorporating vibration-isolating handles.

53 Choose grinding wheels carefully. Residual imbalance in the grinding wheel can be a major cause of high vibration in portable grinders and the initial imbalance can persist throughout the lives of the wheels.

54 When buying powered screwdrivers, nut runners and torque wrenches for assembly work, select rotary action rather than impact or impulse action tools. Additional benefits, such as a significant reduction in noise levels, can be obtained.

55 Finally, select vibration-damped chisels and similar tools where possible.

Process control

56 Good process control is important for maintaining product quality, production efficiency and controlling vibration exposure. In foundry work, for example, lack of care during the moulding process can considerably increase the amount of fettling needed.

Maintenance

57 Regular servicing will help keep vibration levels down to the minimum necessary for efficient operation. Equipment suppliers can be asked to provide maintenance schedules.

58 The following measures also help keep down vibration exposures:

- keeping cutting tools sharp;

- dressing grinding wheels correctly by following manufacturers' recommendations;

- replacing worn parts;

- carrying out necessary balance checks and corrections;

- replacing anti-vibration mounts and suspended handles before they deteriorate. Look for deterioration

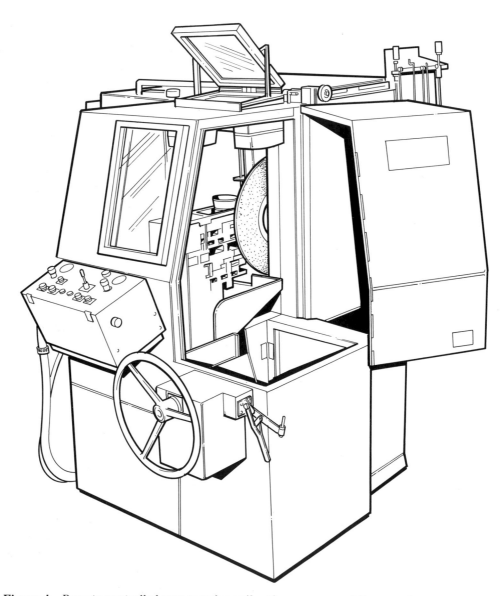

Figure 4 *Remote-controlled saw to reduce vibration exposure of the operator*

or the cracking, swelling and softening (or hardening) of rubber mounts;

■ checking and replacing defective vibration dampers, bearings and gears;

■ sharpening chain-saw teeth and keeping the correct chain tension;

■ tuning engines.

REDUCING VIBRATION TRANSMISSION TO THE HAND

General

59 The most effective way to prevent vibration reaching workers' hands is to avoid using processes which require workers to hold vibrating surfaces. The amount of vibration actually passing to the hand and arm depends on:

■ the magnitude and frequency of vibration of the surfaces which are being held;

■ forces exerted by the hand in gripping, pushing, guiding and supporting the vibrating tool, handle or workpiece;

■ the posture adopted by the worker;

■ characteristics of the connection between the worker's hand and the surface held.

60 Jigs and similar aids incorporating anti-vibration mounts can help avoid the need to grip vibrating surfaces. Wrapping rubber or other resilient materials around vibrating handles may reduce high-frequency vibration but is unlikely to reduce significantly vibration transmission in the range of frequencies likely to lead to the development of HAVS. In some cases it may be possible to fit 'anti-vibration' handles to tools retrospectively, but take care to ensure that the handle is matched to the vibration characteristics of the tool.

61 The greater the forces exerted through the hand onto the vibrating surface, the greater the vibration passing into the user's hand and arm. These forces may be required either to support the tool or workpiece, to control or guide the machine, or to achieve high metal removal rates.

62 The actual forces applied can be greater than is essential for efficient work because of incorrect equipment selection, inadequate maintenance, insufficient training or poor work station design. Some of the ways in which improvements might be made are:

■ where heavy workpieces are hand ground at pedestal grinders, support for the whole piece will mean that the worker needs only to guide the article onto the wheel rather than support all the weight;

■ tension chains (sometimes called balancers) and manipulators can be used to support vibrating tools such as heavy drills, nut runners, nailing guns and (in some cases) pneumatic chisels, thus eliminating the burden imposed by the tool's weight;

■ changes in the texture and material of a grip surface may allow the operator to use a lighter grip to hold and control the tool.

Training

63 Instruction and training for workers in working techniques can help avoid excessive grip pressures and push and guiding forces. Workers can also be encouraged to use the lightest tool capable of doing the work; to rest the tool as much as possible on the material being worked (or in the case of hand-held workpieces, on any support provided); and to hold it with a light but safe grip.

Anti-vibration gloves

64 Anti-vibration gloves usually provide little attenuation at the most hazardous frequencies and in some cases may increase the vibration reaching the hand. They are not usually an effective way to reduce vibration exposure.

REDUCING THE PERIOD OF EXPOSURE

65 Job rotation or other management techniques can also help to keep vibration exposures down. Careful planning and supervision of the workers' activities will be needed to make these controls effective.

CHAPTER THREE

Clinical effects and the health surveillance programme

KEY POINTS

- HAVS comprises vascular, neurological and musculoskeletal components.

- The longer a worker is exposed to hand-transmitted vibration, the worse the symptoms become.

- The degree to which symptoms regress on removal from exposure is not known with certainty, but neurological symptoms possibly do not improve while vascular symptoms may do so.

- The Stockholm Workshop scales should be used to classify HAVS symptoms.

- Other systems for classifying vascular symptoms include the Taylor-Pelmear assessment scale and the method described by Griffin.

- Medical management of workers showing symptoms should include:

  - establishing review periods to monitor the rate of progression;

  - advising workers individually about the likely effects of continuing to work with high vibration;

  - recommending that workers stop exposure if this is likely to cause disease progressing to Stockholm stage 3 vascular or sensorineural;

  - providing employers with anonymous grouped information about the incidence of symptoms in the workforce.

INTRODUCTION

66   This chapter advises occupational health professionals on the clinical effects of hand-transmitted vibration and implementation of a health surveillance programme for workers exposed to hand-arm vibration. The term 'HAVS' has been used to describe the effects of hand-transmitted vibration on the upper limb but is not clearly defined. In the United Kingdom, HAVS is considered to exist if, after prolonged exposure to hand-transmitted vibration, involvement of the vascular and/or peripheral nervous system occurs, with or without musculoskeletal involvement.

67   The symptoms result from pathological effects on the peripheral vascular system, peripheral nervous system, muscles, bones, tendons and soft tissues. Episodic finger blanching is the most widely known of these effects, but the sensory changes are now being given greater importance. A particular worker who has signs or symptoms of one or more of the possible effects of hand-transmitted vibration on the upper limb may be considered as suffering from HAVS. This description should then be qualified to show the body system affected.

CLINICAL EFFECTS OF HAND-TRANSMITTED VIBRATION

Hand-arm vibration syndrome: vascular component

68   Episodic finger blanching is the characteristic vascular sign. Initially this presents as transient pallor of the tip of one or more fingers. As the condition progresses, so does the area affected, extending to include the whole of the distal, middle and finally also the proximal phalange and very occasionally beyond. The thumb may also be affected. The parts affected tend to be those in closest contact with vibration.

69   After initial blanching, the circulation is restored, either spontaneously after a variable period of time which can be more than thirty minutes, or after rewarming the finger. Tissue ischaemia during the period of spasm results in an exaggerated return of blood flow and painful red throbbing fingers (reactive hyperaemia). Despite considerable research, the disorder of physiology which underlies the intermittent peripheral ischaemia is not known. Between the periods of spasm and reactive hyperaemia there may be a cyanotic (blue) phase in which a dusky blue colour results from the increased extraction of oxygen from the sluggish capillary circulation. The sequence of colour change seen in the finger is often white, purple and red. After exposure to high vibration for a period of years, a chronic permanent dusky discoloration of the affected fingers may result.

70   The main trigger for the symptoms is exposure to cold, for example on the way to work early on a winter's morning. Although vibration causes the condition, it does not precipitate the symptoms. As the condition progresses, the frequency of attack will increase. Vasospasm may be triggered by localised or general body cooling in otherwise warm environments. During attacks the sufferer may complain of pain, numbness and cold as well as reduced manual dexterity and loss of finger co-ordination.

71   Similar symptoms can occur spontaneously from a variety of causes including Raynaud's disease or constitutional white finger (primary Raynaud's phenomenon). Raynaud's disease affects up to five per cent of males and ten per cent of females, although higher prevalences have been reported. It usually affects the fingers bilaterally but can sometimes affect the toes as well. Emotional factors and the cold may provoke the symptoms which may begin in adolescence. A number of conditions are recognised which may cause such vascular symptoms secondarily. These are then described as secondary Raynaud's phenomenon (see Table 2). Although many of these conditions are rare, all need to be considered in the differential diagnosis of the vascular component.

Neurological component

72   Neurological symptoms of HAVS include tingling, numbness, loss of sensation and manual dexterity. Painful parasthesiae may disturb sleep.

Such symptoms are thought to develop independently of the vascular changes and may not regress on removal from exposure to vibration. The neurological changes cause impaired functional ability in the hand. As with the vascular component, the symptoms attributed to hand-transmitted vibration may also arise from some medical conditions. The main disease groups concerned are given in Table 3.

73   Vibration may damage the mechanoreceptors in the skin or the sensory nerve fibres, but the relative importance of effects on these structures in the aetiology of sensory symptoms is not yet established.

Muscular and soft tissue component

74   Studies of forestry workers have identified complaints of muscle fatigue and reductions in hand grip strength after chronic exposure to vibration. These findings suggest that there may be an effect of vibration on muscle function but the mechanism and the extent to which workers in other occupations may be affected are not known.

75   Carpal tunnel syndrome, Dupytren's contracture and trigger finger have all been reported in studies of vibration-exposed workers but a causal relationship has only been accepted for carpal tunnel syndrome.

Skeletal component

76   This comprises disorders of the bones (cysts and vacuoles) and joints of the upper limb. Such effects may arise

Table 2   *Secondary Raynaud's phenomenon**

Connective tissue disease	Traumatic
Scleroderma	Following injury or surgery
Mixed connective tissue disease	Hand-transmitted vibration
Systemic lupus erythematosus	Frostbite
Rheumatoid arthritis	Thoracic outlet syndrome
Dermatomyositis	
Polyarteritis nodosa	**Toxins/drugs**
Sjogren's disease	Vinyl chloride
	Ergot
Arterial disease	Beta-blockers
Thrombo-angiitis obliterans	Clonidine
Thrombo-embolism	
Arteriosclerosis	**Neurogenic**
	Poliomyelitis
Dysglobulinaemia	Syringomyelia
Cryoglobulinaemia	Hemiplegia

Table 3   *Possible causes of neurological symptoms similar to those encountered in HAVS**

Peripheral nerve entrapment	Peripheral neuropathy
Carpal tunnel syndrome	Diabetic
Ulnar nerve entrapment at elbow or wrist	Alcoholic
Thoracic outlet syndrome	Toxic (eg organophosphates, thallium,
	acrylamide, carbon disulphide, n-hexane,
Central nervous system disorders	methyl butyl ketone, diethyl thiocarbamate,
Compression myelopathy (spondylosis or	lead)
spinal cord tumour)	Drug induced (eg chloramphenicol,
Subacute combined degeneration of the cord	isoniazid, streptomycin, polymyxin,
Multiple sclerosis	ethambutol, nitrofurantoin, metronidazole,
	gold, indomethacin, vincristine, perhexiline,
Injuries to the arm and neck	phenytoin)

* Reproduced with permission from the report of a working party of the Faculty of Occupational Medicine of the Royal College of Physicians, *Hand transmitted vibration: clinical effects and pathophysiology. Part 1: Report of a working party.*

from the manual handling of heavy tools, but percussive vibration has also been implicated. Peri-articular ossification may result in a reduced range of motion of the elbow joint. This may be unsuspected if not specifically elicited at examinations.

Prognosis

77   After the onset of vascular and neurological symptoms, the longer an individual is exposed to vibration, the worse the symptoms become. The degree to which symptoms regress on removal from exposure to vibration is not known with any certainty. The present limited evidence suggests that the neurological symptoms do not improve, but that vascular symptoms may do so after some years have elapsed. This is thought to be the case if the individual is below 50 years of age and the vascular symptoms have not progressed to stage 3 of the Stockholm Workshop scale.

'Vibration disease'

78   A generalised syndrome of 'vibration disease' is said to include symptoms such as fatigue, vertigo and headache, the cause of which is difficult to establish, as is the link with vibration. This is not generally accepted in the United Kingdom. There is also a suggestion that vibration-exposed workers who develop vascular symptoms of HAVS may develop noise-induced hearing loss more rapidly than other exposed workers without symptoms.

CLASSIFICATION OF SYMPTOMS

79   In 1975 Taylor and Pelmear published a report on vibration white finger in selected British industries.[5] This included an assessment scale for the symptoms of VWF (see Table 4) which subsequently found general acceptance in the United Kingdom. Symptoms were graded according to the extent of the blanching and its association with neurological effects, the seasonal influence on blanching and the degree of interference with work and social activities.

80   Since then it has been appreciated that the vascular and neurological components of HAVS progress separately, and it is no longer considered satisfactory to rely on seasonal or subjective factors for classification. A new classification scheme, the Stockholm Workshop scales (see Table 5) is now replacing the Taylor-Pelmear scale and should be used to classify the vascular and neurological symptoms of HAVS. The two hands require separate assessment. The grade of the vascular disorder is indicated by the stages of both hands and the number of affected fingers on each hand.

81   One difficulty with progressive scales is the limited number of points available to cater for the varying extent and frequency of symptoms. The Stockholm vascular scale relies on a count of the number of fingers affected on each hand to give the full classification. An alternative approach is

Table 4   *Taylor-Pelmear classification of vibration white finger by stages*

Stage	Condition of digits	Work/social interference
0	No blanching	None
0T	Intermittent tingling	None
0N	Intermittent numbness	None
0TN	Tingling and numbness	None
1	Blanching of one or more fingertips, with or without tingling and numbness	None
2	Blanching of one or more fingers with numbness usually confined to winter	Slight interference with home and social activities, no interference with work
3	Extensive blanching, frequent episodes in summer and winter	Definite interference at work, at home and with social/recreational activities
4	Extensive blanching most fingers, frequent episodes in summer and winter, finger ulcerations	Occupational change to avoid further vibration exposure because of severity of signs and symptoms

Table 5   *The Stockholm Workshop scales*

Vascular component		
Stage	**Grade**	**Description**
0		No attacks
1V	Mild	Occasional attacks affecting only the tips of one or more fingers
2V	Moderate	Occasional attacks affecting distal and middle (rarely also proximal) phalanges of one or more fingers
3V	Severe	Frequent attacks affecting all phalanges of most fingers
4V	Very severe	As in stage 3 with trophic changes in the fingertips

Sensorineural component	
Stage	**Description**
0SN	Vibration-exposed but no symptoms
1SN	Intermittent numbness with or without tingling
2SN	Intermittent or persistent numbness, reduced sensory perception
3SN	Intermittent or persistent numbness, reduced tactile discrimination and/or manipulative dexterity

Notes for Table 5 The staging is made separately for each hand. The grade of disorder is indicated by the stage and number of affected fingers on both hands, eg stage/handling/number of digits.

to allocate a weighted numerical value to each phalange affected and calculate an overall score as in the method described by Griffin (see Figure 5). This caters only for the extent of blanching, but is easily derived and may be a useful supplement to the Stockholm classification.

DIAGNOSIS OF HAND-ARM VIBRATION SYNDROME

82 In the absence of an attack of blanching there may be no clinical signs of disease affecting the vascular system.

Objective test methods, such as those described briefly in Appendix 2, have been developed in an attempt to overcome this problem. The final diagnosis depends ultimately on the judgement of the medical examiner taking into account both the reported symptoms and the findings on clinical examination, including objective testing where appropriate.

83 Routine assessment is helped by using a standardised questionnaire on which to record information about the individual's history of exposure to hand-transmitted vibration at work, any leisure time exposure, current medication, any symptomatology and the

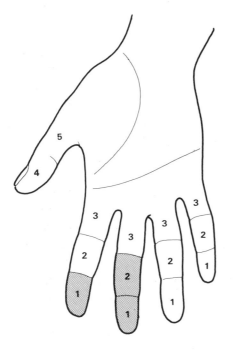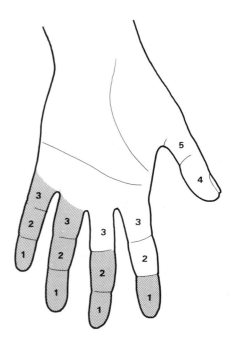

Figure 5 *Numerical scoring of vascular symptoms of HAVS*

Notes for Figure 5 The magnitude of blanching for a digit is given a numerical value as indicated above, and a total score for each hand is assigned. In the above example, it is possible to write the scores in the following manner 01300_R and 01366_L.

results of a clinical examination. An example of a suitable questionnaire is given in Appendix 3. The reported history of symptoms is the most useful diagnostic information. Clinical examination will be directed at vascular and neurological function in the arm and hand and a number of specific tests may be appropriate.

84   The extent to which further tests relevant to the differential diagnosis of HAVS are appropriate in routine surveillance will depend on the discretion of the examining physician. Where non-occupational conditions are suspected, the worker's general practitioner should be informed.

85   The use of objective methods may help to monitor a vibration-exposed population and to assess the progress or regression of disease in response to a changed vibration exposure.

TREATMENT OF HAND-ARM VIBRATION SYNDROME

86   Although research is continuing, there is little effective treatment for the vascular symptoms of HAVS. There is no treatment for its neurological component.

HEALTH SURVEILLANCE PROGRAMME

General

87   The first approach to prevent HAVS is to control vibration exposure. However, knowledge of the dose response relationship from exposure to vibration is incomplete and cannot be relied on to prevent symptoms in all workers. The aim of health surveillance is to stop significant handicap. Both pre-employment and routine monitoring of exposed workers are recommended.

88   If health surveillance is to be introduced in an already exposed workforce, workers or their representatives should be consulted to ensure that they are aware of the purpose and methods of surveillance, and of action that may be required for the control of disease, such as redeployment. During health surveillance, workers should be informed of the results of each assessment and/or examination and of any implications of the findings, such as a requirement to modify or reduce vibration exposure. There should also be an opportunity to discuss such implications at the time when health assessments are made.

89   Health surveillance should be directed by a qualified medical practitioner, preferably one who has experience and training in occupational medicine. An occupational health nurse,

trained in methods of clinical assessment required for routine surveillance, may make such assessments under the direction of a medical practitioner. Decisions regarding suitability for employment or redeployment from vibration exposure will be the responsibility of the medical practitioner.

Pre-employment assessment

90 It is recommended that individuals who suffer from Raynaud's disease or Raynaud's phenomenon of non-occupational origin should not be exposed to hand-transmitted vibration at work. Raynaud's phenomenon may occur in some individuals as a side effect of medication such as Beta-blockers. Pre-employment assessment by questionnaire and clinical examination will identify these individuals and establish a baseline from which to judge the results of routine assessment. It also provides an opportunity to educate workers about the health effects of hand-arm vibration, and about measures which are under a worker's control and which will help to minimise the onset of symptoms. Smoking in vibration-exposed workers should be discouraged as it affects blood circulation.

Routine assessment

91 It is recommended that this should be performed annually. For newly-exposed workers, a check after six months to identify any worker who may be particularly susceptible should also be considered. The need for this can be judged in the light of the expected latent

interval for the onset of vascular symptoms which is a function of the frequency-weighted vibration acceleration magnitude. More frequent assessments may be appropriate after the onset of symptoms in order to judge the rate of progression and the effect of any workplace intervention. Assessment should be by means of questionnaire and clinical examination as at the pre-employment stage. Shorter screening questionnaires can be used at this stage. In the absence of reported symptoms, there is no need for further assessment. Workers should be encouraged to report any symptoms to a designated person at any time.

MANAGEMENT OF THE AFFECTED WORKER

92 When symptoms are first reported, exposure conditions should be re-assessed and a period for review established. The rate of progression of symptoms and any functional impairment should be monitored. Where vascular and neurological symptoms are both present they may progress at different rates. Measures to reduce the individual vibration exposure should be considered if reasonably practicable.

93 At the onset of vascular or neurological symptoms at stage 2 on the Stockholm scales, re-assess exposure conditions. If symptoms have progressed rapidly and there is little scope to reduce exposure, it may be prudent for the individual to cease work with vibration at this point. Where progress has been less rapid and if there is a response to exposure reduction, continuing exposure under regular surveillance may be permissible.

94 Workers should be advised individually about the likely effects of their continuing to work with hand-transmitted vibration once symptoms have begun. Whether an individual should stop work entailing exposure will depend on the progression of symptoms and their functional effect. It is not advisable for workers to continue exposure if this is likely to result in disease progressing to Stockholm stage 3, vascular or sensorineural.

95 Health professionals also have a role in educating workers, supplementing the training provided by the employer. Health professionals may also provide employers with feed-back about the incidence of symptoms in the workforce to close the loop on control. Anonymous grouped results of health surveillance can be divulged to the employer without individual consent, to be used as a basis to assess the adequacy of control measures over time in different locations. The detailed results of individual health surveillance remain, however, 'medical in confidence' and should only be divulged to the employer with the permission of the worker concerned.

CHAPTER FOUR

Measuring hand-arm vibration

KEY POINTS

- The average magnitude of vibration is indicated by the root-mean-square (rms) frequency-weighted acceleration.

- Vibration accelerometers measure vibration along a single axis.

- The total vibration can be determined by measuring along three orthogonal axes and combining the results to give a single overall acceleration level.

- Correct selection and mounting of the accelerometer is important.

- Vibration exposure A(8) can be calculated from the vibration measurements and the duration of exposure.

INTRODUCTION

96 This chapter gives advice for technicians on measurement of hand-transmitted vibration exposure, in accordance with British Standard BS 6842:1987. In some cases it is advisable to use more advanced techniques, particularly for highly percussive tools or for complex work cycles.

WHAT IS MEASURED?

97 Exposure to hand-transmitted vibration is quantified in terms of the acceleration of the surface in contact with the hand. The acceleration of the surface is normally expressed in units of metres per second squared (m/s^2).

98 The extent of damage caused to the hand and arm depends on the frequency of the energy being transmitted from the vibrating surface. Low-frequency motion, from about 5 to 20 Hertz (cycles per second or Hz) is thought to be potentially more damaging than higher frequency motion. Vibration at frequencies below 2 Hz and above 1500 Hz is not thought to cause damage. To allow for this frequency dependence, a frequency weighting is applied to measurements of vibration magnitude (see Figure 6).

99 The average magnitude of the vibration is indicated by the root-mean-square (rms) acceleration value and should be measured with the frequency weighting applied. Such a vibration measurement is represented as $a_{h,w}$,

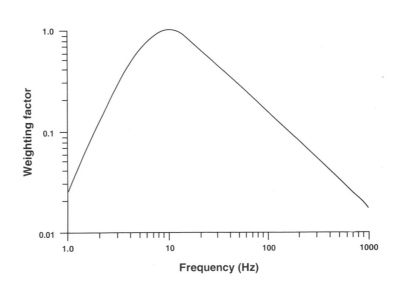

Frequency (Hz)	Weighting factor
8	1.030
10	1.022
12.5	0.987
16	0.902
20	0.785
25	0.625
31.5	0.523
40	0.411
50	0.327
63	0.258
80	0.202
100	0.161
125	0.129
160	0.100
200	0.080
250	0.064
315	0.051
400	0.040
500	0.032
630	0.025
800	0.020
1000	0.016

Figure 6 *Frequency weighting function and table of weighting factors*

where the 'h' indicates hand-transmitted vibration and the 'w' indicates that the measurement has been frequency weighted.

100 Accelerometers are sensitive to acceleration along a single axis. To assess the total vibration entering the hand, measure along the three orthogonal axes, x, y and z (see Figure 7). The frequency-weighted acceleration along the z-axis, for example, would then be represented as $a_{z,h,w}$.

101 It is often useful to combine the results from the three measurement axes to give an overall acceleration, given by:

$$a_{h,w} = \sqrt{a^2_{x,h,w} + a^2_{y,h,w} + a^2_{z,h,w}}$$

102 The damage caused by hand-transmitted vibration is related to the average vibration magnitude a person is exposed to during the working day. This is referred to as the daily vibration exposure. To assess daily vibration exposure, the 8 hour energy equivalent acceleration $(a_{h,w})_{eq(8)}$, or more simply A(8), is determined. This quantity accounts for both the vibration magnitude and the time over which the exposure takes place.

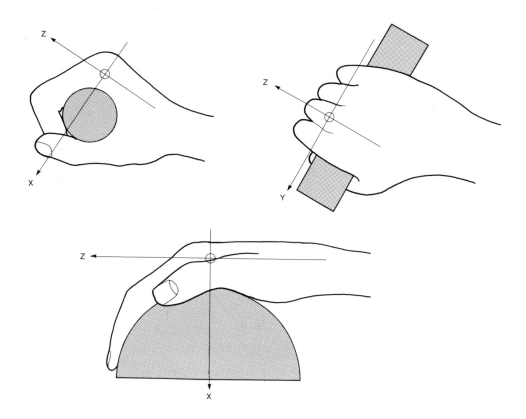

Figure 7 *Co-ordinate system*

INSTRUMENTATION

103 A simple instrument for measuring vibration (see Figure 8) comprises five elements. They are:

■ **accelerometer:** a device which attaches to the vibrating surface and produces an output proportional to the acceleration;

■ **pre-amplifier:** an initial amplification stage designed to accept the signal from the accelerometer and convert it into a voltage proportional to the acceleration;

■ **frequency weighting:** applies the hand-transmitted vibration frequency weighting to the acceleration signal;

■ **time averaging**: provides rms averaging of the input acceleration. Short averages allow the changes in vibration magnitude to be observed, while longer averages will give an indication of overall vibration exposure;

■ **display**: presents the measured vibration magnitude in m/s^2 or the level, $L_{h,w}$ in decibels (dB), where:

$$L_{h,w} = 20L\,og\,_{10}\frac{a_{h,w}}{a_0}$$

and

$$a_0 = 10^{-6} \text{ m/s}^2.$$

104 British Standard BS 7482:1991[6] provides a specification for vibration measurement instrumentation. Where possible, use instruments which conform to this or an equivalent standard, such as in ISO 8041.[7]

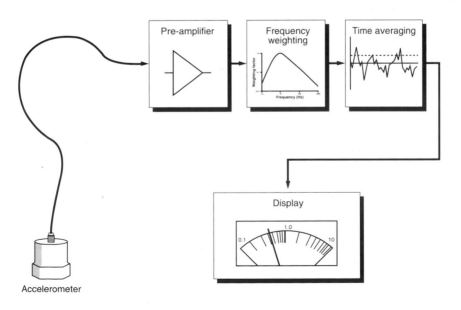

Figure 8 *Block diagram of vibration instrument*

MEASUREMENT PROCESS

105 The measurement of vibration exposure can be divided into five stages:

■ identifying a series of **discrete operations** which make up the subject's normal working pattern;

■ measuring the **vibration magnitude** for each operation identified;

■ assessing typical **daily exposure time** for each operation;

■ calculating **partial vibration exposure** for each operation;

■ calculating **8 hour vibration exposure** for the subject.

Identifying discrete operations

106 Any daily job consists of a series of operations. For hand-transmitted vibration assessments, identify all operations involving hand contact with vibrating surfaces. For each operation, measure the vibration magnitude. Where a task is repetitive, consisting of a cycle of operations, each element of the cycle must be identified and measured. Having identified the operations which make up a daily work pattern, measure the average vibration magnitude of each operation.

Measuring vibration magnitude

107 Before measuring hand-transmitted vibration there are a number of questions which need to be addressed:

Which accelerometers are appropriate?

108 Hand-held tools can produce high vibration magnitudes. A pneumatic hammer, for example, may generate a maximum acceleration of 20 000 to 50 000 m/s^2. However, much of this energy is at frequencies well outside the range relevant to hand-transmitted vibration. The accelerometer chosen for the measurement must be able, therefore, to operate at these very high-vibration magnitudes and yet still respond to the much lower magnitudes in the 2 to 1500 Hz range.

109 The choice of accelerometer is very important. If its sensitivity is too high, the acceleration signal may become distorted, affecting the measured magnitude. Accelerometers specifically designed for measuring shock vibration should be avoided. To allow them to measure very high accelerations, shock accelerometers have very low sensitivities and so cannot respond to the low-level, low-frequency vibrations which are important when measuring hand-transmitted vibration.

110 Accelerometer selection will also be influenced by the 'mounted resonance frequency' of the accelerometer. Generally this should be more than three times the maximum frequency of interest. However, for hand-transmitted vibration measurements the mounted resonance frequency should be much higher, ideally 30 000 to 50 000 Hz.

111 Fitting an accelerometer to a vibrating surface alters the vibrational characteristics of that surface. The lighter the accelerometer, the smaller the error introduced. Therefore, the mass of the accelerometer should be as low as possible, ideally less than ten per cent of the mass of the object.

112 In most measurements, therefore, use general purpose accelerometers capable of withstanding acceleration shocks up to about 100 000 m/s^2, with a mounted resonance frequency of greater than 30 000 Hz and weighing less than 20 g.

Are mechanical filters necessary?

113 Any accelerometer suitable for measuring hand-transmitted vibration will respond to frequencies far higher than the 1500 Hz maximum required by the measurement. When fitted beneath an accelerometer, mechanical filters reduce the high-frequency vibrations reaching the accelerometer while allowing low-frequency information to pass unaffected. They are particularly valuable when measurements are carried out on percussive tools where a distortion of the acceleration signal, known as 'dc shift' can occur. The mechanical filters reduce the impulsive acceleration which is known to cause dc shift. The cut-off frequency (the frequency above which the vibrations are reduced) of a mechanical filter depends on the mass of the accelerometer; the lighter the accelerometer, the higher the cut-off frequency.

Are triaxial measurements necessary?

114 Where possible, measure simultaneously along all three axes. However, there are situations where triaxial measurement is not possible or even necessary, for example on very light objects. To avoid adding excessive mass, measure in one direction at a time. Some tools, such as pneumatic chisels, have an obvious highest axis of vibration. Measurement along the highest axis alone will be sufficient if the magnitude is more than twice that along both of the other two axes (this will need to be determined by trial measurements).

Is the measurement system working and calibrated?

115 Calibration of a vibration measurement system may be carried out by using either the manufacturer's sensitivity specification for the accelerometer, or a vibration calibrator. The accelerometer sensitivity is provided in terms of either picocoulombs per metre per second squared (pC/ms^{-2}) or millivolts per metre per second squared (mV/ms^{-2}). With appropriate instrumentation, the charge (Coulombs) or voltage (Volts) sensitivity can be set directly. Once the sensitivity has been set, the instrument is ready for use. However, where possible, use a vibration calibrator, or some known acceleration input, to confirm the accelerometer sensitivity and to provide a full check of both the accelerometer and the measuring instrument. With measurement systems based on piezo-resistive accelerometers, inverting the accelerometer will give a change in reading of twice the acceleration due to gravity (2 g or 19.6 m/s^2).

116 A full calibration of equipment, which should be done periodically, can only be verified in a properly equipped laboratory. Decide how often a full calibration is needed and whether equipment is being used in conditions particularly likely to cause deterioration. Take account of information available on how long the instrument and accelerometers can be expected to maintain their performance (the supplier can be asked about this). Restrict the interval between full calibration to no more than two years.

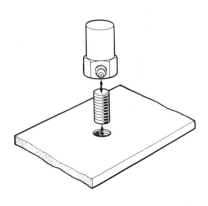

Stud mounting
Uses: Workpieces such as castings
Advantages: Good frequent response
Disadvantages: Surface must be drilled and tapped

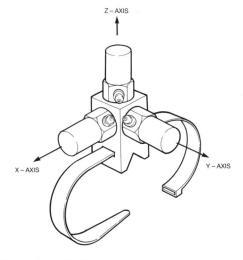

Hose clip/cable tie mount
Uses: Tool handles
Advantages: Can be used for triaxial measurements
Disadvantages: Can be bulky and heavy

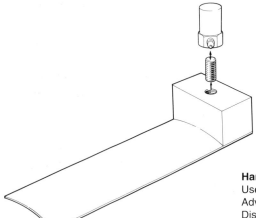

Hand-held mount
Uses: Tool handles
Advantages: Can be used on anti-vibration materials
Disadvantages: Poor frequency response

Figure 9 *Methods of fixing accelerometers*

How should accelerometers be fitted?

117 There are many ways to fix accelerometers to hand tools or components (see Figure 9). The method used depends on the particular measurement situation. Each method has its own advantages and disadvantages and none is perfect. Attach the accelerometers firmly to the vibrating surface, as near as possible to the point of contact with the hand. Where appropriate, consider the left and right hands separately.

Where should accelerometer cables be routed?

118 If accelerometer cables are allowed to vibrate, capacitance changes in the cables caused by that vibration (the triboelectric effect) will result in additional measured vibration. In addition, the accelerometer cables should not be bent sharply, twisted or otherwise stressed as this will degrade their performance. They must be taped down to the vibrating surface, near to the accelerometer. A clear route between the workpiece and the measuring instrumentation should be provided. For pneumatically-powered hand tools, fixing the cables at regular intervals along the air supply line is generally effective.

What measurement range is appropriate?

119 Most instruments allow the user to select the maximum acceleration magnitude that the instrument can measure. This setting defines the measurement range of the instrument. The appropriate measurement range can be determined by performing trial measurements. To obtain the best signal-to-noise performance, select the lowest possible range.

120 It is important to make use of overload detection built into the instrument as accelerometers are sensitive to a frequency range much wider than that required by the measurements. It is common for very high-frequency signals to cause an overload at the input stages of the instrument, giving an overload indication when the frequency-weighted acceleration measurement is low.

How long should measurement be?

121 A measurement should be an average over a period which is representative of the typical use of a tool or process. Where possible, the measurement period should start when the worker's hands first contact the vibrating surface and finish when contact is broken. This period may include variations in the vibration magnitude and may even include periods when there is no exposure. Ideally, the measurements should be averaged over several minutes of exposure, with repeat measurements made to confirm the results. Measurements made for less than 15 seconds will be highly unreliable in their assessment of low-frequency components.

Assessing daily exposure time

122 Vibration exposures are usually for short periods, often repeated many times during a working day. Although measurements can be averaged over complete cycles of operation (including periods when the vibration source is switched off), normally it is only possible to average over the short period that the hand is in contact with the vibrating surface.

123 Whichever method is used for vibration measurement, the total exposure time per day must be found. Where the vibration has been averaged over a complete cycle of work, the daily exposure time is simply the duration of the work cycle multiplied by the number of cycles per day. If a measurement has been made for a period while the hand is in contact with the vibrating surface, assess the total contact time per day.

Calculating partial vibration exposure

124 In many cases a worker's daily exposure comes from a number of sources. For each vibration source, find the average acceleration magnitude and the exposure time to that source per day.

The partial vibration exposure, $A_i(8)$ is then found using either the nomogram in Figure 10 or:

$$A_i(8) = a_{h,w}\sqrt{\frac{t}{8}}$$

where t is the daily exposure time (in hours) to the vibration magnitude $a_{h,w}$. The partial vibration exposure represents the contribution of a particular source of vibration to the total daily exposure.

Calculating daily vibration exposure

125 Having determined the partial vibration exposure values for each vibration source a subject is exposed to, the daily vibration exposure can be calculated using:

$$A(8) = \sqrt{A_1(8)^2 + A_2(8)^2 + A_3(8)^2}$$

where $A_1(8)$, $A_2(8)$ and $A_3(8)$, are the partial vibration exposure values for each vibration source.

126 Assess the daily exposure for both hands of a subject, given in terms of the highest axis vibration. Where there is no clear highest axis, also report the vector sum daily vibration exposure.

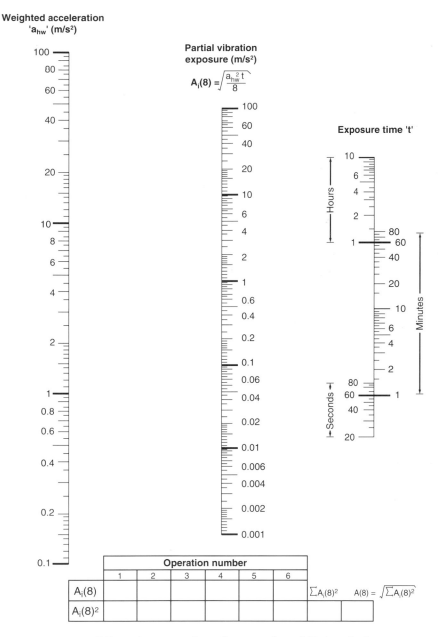

1) For each exposure, draw a line connecting weighted acceleration with exposure time. Read off the partial vibration exposure, $A_i(8)$, given by the point where the line crosses the centre scale.
2) Square and add all partial vibration exposures.
3) Square root result to give daily vibration exposure.

Figure 10 *Nomogram for calculating daily vibration exposure*

APPENDICES

APPENDIX ONE: Purchasing new tools and equipment

When purchasing new tools and equipment, employers should ask suppliers for information on vibration. The following list suggests some possible questions.

1 Is the vibration of any handle or other surface to be held by the user likely to exceed an acceleration of 2.5 m/s^2, in normal use?

If the answer to question 1 is YES,

2 What is the frequency-weighted acceleration:

(a) under operating conditions producing the highest vibration?

(b) under typical operating conditions?

(c) under other standard conditions?

3 Under what operating conditions were the measurements made?

4 If the tests were in accordance with a published standard, provide details and indicate the extent to which the vibration may differ from the quoted values under normal conditions of use.

5 What measures have been taken to minimise vibration?

6 Are additional vibration reduction measures practicable? Give details of any design changes, the additional cost and any production penalties.

7 What is the maximum frequency-weighted acceleration that the tool or equipment can be guaranteed not to exceed?

8 What tests would be carried out to confirm any claims made in answer to question 7?

9 What other measures are required to minimise the vibration hazard to which employees are exposed when using the tool or equipment in question? Give details of any special maintenance requirements.

APPENDIX TWO:
Objective test methods for diagnosis of hand-arm vibration syndrome

1 The objective methods described here require special equipment and facilities and are not intended for use in routine workplace surveillance for the clinical effects of HAVS. Such methods will have a role in the assessment of either the progress of disease or regression after removal from exposure. They should be considered where an individual's continuing exposure to vibration is in question. For full details of the test methods described, refer to scientific and medical literature.

Vascular component

Cold provocation testing

2 The purpose of this technique is to demonstrate objectively an abnormal response of the finger to cold stimulation. In most methods, the whole hand is immersed in cold water and the fall in finger temperature and the pattern of recovery after removal from the water is monitored. Several parameters can be calculated including the time taken for the finger to gain a certain temperature or to recover a certain percentage of the fallen temperature. Although blanching may occur during cold provocation testing, its occurrence is an unreliable indicator of disease.

3 For reliable results it is essential that the test takes place in a warm room and that the subject is also warm.

Body heating may be used to raise finger temperature if this is low. The temperature of the water used and the duration of immersion are not yet standardised. In addition, arterial occlusion is applied during cold water immersion in some tests. The sensitivity of cold provocation testing varies from 60 to 80 per cent.

Other blood flow methods

4 Superficial blood flow can be recorded using a photocell plethysmograph which can, for example, be incorporated into a cold provocation test. Total finger blood flow can be measured using a strain gauge plethysmograph. With the addition of cuffs to occlude arterial inflow and control finger temperature, detailed assessment of the blood flow response in an individual finger can be made, including measurement of finger systolic blood pressure. The response of affected and non-affected fingers, as controls, can be compared in the same individual.

Neurological component

Aesthesiometry

5 Two point and depth sense perception can be tested using an aesthesiometer of the type described by Carlson.[8] Although normal values have been published, these should be confirmed for the particular device in use. Results would be useful on a longitudinal basis and in comparing groups, but single measures will not have diagnostic significance.

Vibrotactile threshold measurement

6   This technique measures the sensitivity of skin mechanoreceptors to a vibration stimulus. This is performed using a small vibrating probe against which the finger is applied at a constant pressure. The intensity of vibration is varied in a manner similar to the variation of the auditory stimulus in Bekesy Audiometry. The results are age dependent and subject to a temporary threshold shift from previous vibration exposure. They can be used to differentiate groups of workers with different exposure experience, but are not diagnostic on an individual basis.

Temperature threshold measurement

7   Temperature sensitivity in the fingers may be abnormal in HAVS. Thermal pain thresholds may be elevated and the temperature neutral zone widened. Testing requires the use of a specially-constructed probe in which the rate of change of temperature can be controlled. The subject responds by activating a switch when a cold or warm sensation is felt.

Electrophysiology

8   Measurement of the conduction velocity in the median nerve is a standard technique for diagnosing carpal tunnel syndrome and suitable apparatus is available in many neurology departments. Both motor and sensory conduction velocities in the median and ulnar nerves have been reported to have decreased in workers exposed to HAVS, but such changes are not specific to vibration damage.

Skeletal system

9   Radiology of the upper limb is not recommended in routine surveillance.

APPENDIX THREE: Health surveillance questionnaire

MEDICAL CONFIDENTIAL
ASSESSMENT OF HAND-ARM VIBRATION

DATE

1*   Mr/Mrs/Miss/Ms SURNAME _____ FORENAMES_____   M   F

ADDRESS _____

_____ POST CODE _____

DATE OF BIRTH   NI NUMBER _____

ETHNIC GROUP: EUROPEAN ☐   AFRICAN ☐   ASIAN ☐   CARIBBEAN ☐   OTHER ☐

OCCUPATION _____ CHECK/WORKS NO _____ DEPT NO _____

GENERAL PRACTITIONER_____

SECTION A - HAND SYMPTOMS

2*   **1 Blanching**   Yes   No

Have you ever suffered from your fingers going white
on exposure to cold?

If yes, is it continuous?
          episodic?

When did you first notice this? _____ 19 _____

If you suffer now, how often does it occur?   Yes   No

          Several times a year
          Several times a month
          Several times a day
          Every day
          Does it occur in winter only?
          Winter and summer?

State most common circumstances _____

_____

3*   Which fingers are affected?

Right hand   **Left hand**

| Witnessed | |
| Not witnessed | |

Score:	Th	1	2	3	4		Score:	Th	1	2	3	4
Total:							Total:					

MEDICAL CONFIDENTIAL

2 Tingling (excluding transient tingling after using vibrating tool)

	Yes	No
Do you have tingling of the fingers?		
While working?		
In response to cold?		
At other times?		

When did you first notice this? _____ 19 _____

4* Which fingers are affected?

Right hand   **Left hand**

5* **3 Numbness**

	Yes	No
Do your fingers go numb?		
While working?		
In response to cold?		
With blanching?		
At other times?		

If other times, what circumstances? _____

_____

When did you first notice this? _____ 19 _____

Which fingers are affected?

Right hand   **Left hand**

4 Musculoskeletal

	Yes	No
Are you experiencing any other problems with the muscles or joints of your hands/arms?		

	Yes	No			Yes	No
Pain				Stiffness		
Swelling				Weakness		

If yes, give details _____

6* Do you have any difficulty with fine movements of your fingers? | | |

7* Do any of these symptoms (blanching, tingling or numbness) affect your work or leisure activities? | | |
If yes, give details _____

51

MEDICAL CONFIDENTIAL

SECTION B - SOCIAL HISTORY/LEISURE PURSUITS

Yes   No

8*   Do any of your hobbies expose you to hand-arm vibration? ☐☐
If yes, give details _____
_____

Are you a smoker? ☐   Non-smoker? ☐   Ex-smoker? ☐

If ex-smoker when did you stop? _____

9*   Do you drink alcohol?   ☐☐
If yes, how many units per week? _____units/week

SECTION C - MEDICAL HISTORY

Do other members of your family suffer from white finger?   ☐☐
(brothers, sisters and parents only)
If so, who?_____

Have you ever had a neck/arm/hand injury or operation?   ☐☐
If so, what and when? _____

Are there any residual symptoms or deformities?   ☐☐
If so, what? _____

10* Have you ever had any serious disease of:

	Yes No		Yes No		Yes No
Joints?	☐☐	Skin?	☐☐	Nerves?	☐☐

	Yes No		Yes No
Heart or blood vessels?	☐☐	Other?	☐☐

If so give details _____
_____

Are you on any long term medication or treatment for any   ☐☐
condition?

If so, give details: _____

SECTION D - VIBRATION EXPOSURE

Rt   Lt

11* Right handed ☐   Left handed ☐   Leading hand ☐☐

Where do you notice the vibration most? _____

12* Which of the main elements of your present job involve vibration
and how much time a day is spent on vibration work?

Hours

(a) _____   ☐

(b) _____   ☐

When did you join the company? _____ 19_____

MEDICAL CONFIDENTIAL

List main jobs and departments in order

Years

(a) _____ [   ]

(b) _____ [   ]

What jobs did you do previously, outside this company, involving vibration?

Years

(a) _____ [   ]

(b) _____ [   ]

Yes   No

13* Has there been any exposure to neurotoxic agents? [|]

If yes, give details _____

SECTION E - EXAMINATION

14*

Room Temperature °C [   ]

1 Appearance of hands. Note any signs of vascular disease, deformity, scars, callosities or muscle wasting.

Right hand   **Left hand**

2 Describe any abnormality of neck or upper limbs _____

_____

3 Circulation, pulse and blood pressure.

15*

Pulse rate (bpm)		Blood pressure (mm Hg) Lying/sitting	
Rt	[ ]	Rt	[ ]
Lt		Lt	

		Present	Absent		Present	Absent
Radial pulse	Rt			Lt		
Ulnar pulse	Rt			Lt		

16* 4 Nervous system

		Normal	Abnormal		Normal	Abnormal
Light touch	Rt			Lt		
Pin prick	Rt			Lt		
Manual dexterity	Rt			Lt		

(Neurological defect may be recorded on above diagram)

MEDICAL CONFIDENTIAL

17* | 5   Further tests, where appropriate

		Normal	Abnormal			Normal	Abnormal
Lewis Prusik test	Rt			Lt			
Adson's test	Rt			Lt			
Allen's test	Rt			Lt			
Moving 2 point Dis.	Rt			Lt			
Tinel's test	Rt			Lt			
Phalen's test	Rt			Lt			

Grip strength   Rt in Kg [   ]   Lt in Kg [   ]

SECTION F - ASSESSMENT OF HISTORY AND EXAMINATION

Vascular   Yes   No

18* | Primary Raynaud's phenomenon present?
Secondary Raynaud's phenomenon present?
If so, is this vibration induced?

	Left	Right
19* | Severity Stockholm grading (V) | [   ] | [   ] |
20* | Scoring | /33 | /33 |

Cold Provocation Test performed?
Result:_____

_____

Neurological

Neurological impairment suggested by screening tests
Severity, based on screening tests:

21* | Stockholm Neurological grading (SN)   Rt [   ]   Lt [   ]

Musculoskeletal

Muscular or soft tissue disorder present?

NA   Yes   No

Evidence of skeletal disorder (tick if not applicable)

22* | **Latent periods**

Vascular   Years [   ]
Neurological   Years [   ]
Musculoskeletal   Years [   ]

Yes   No

Further special investigations

		Normal	Abnormal			Normal	Abnormal
Aesthesiometry	Rt			Lt			
Vibrotactile threshold	Rt			Lt			
Temperature threshold	Rt			Lt			
Electrophysiological	Rt			Lt			

Fit for work with exposure to hand-transmitted vibration?
Any conditions to be followed? _____
Has advisory leaflet been received by employee?
Date for next medical review_____

Signature   Nursing/Medical Officer

Guidance notes for using health surveillance questionnaire

Please refer to these notes in the course of completion of the health surveillance questionnaire until familiar with its content and use. (The numbers refer to the relevant point in the text, indicated by the figure in the margin.)

1   Personal details Please obtain full information if possible. The National Insurance number may be used in epidemiology and should be sought in all cases. Works numbers may not be allocated in small firms.

2   Blanching This refers to a white discoloration of the fingers usually followed by a red flush. The area affected is variable, sometimes sparing the distal phalanx and occasionally giving a mottled appearance.

3   Diagram Indicate the greatest extent affected at any time (since last assessment). Where part of the phalanx is affected, score as if it blanches completely. Sum the scores of the phalanges of each finger separately to obtain the values for the boxes.

4   Tingling Note which fingers are affected.

5   Numbness This may occur in association with finger blanching or independently. Numbness occurring apart from blanching is of prime interest as this may indicate neurological involvement.

6   Fine movements Difficulties may be experienced, for example, when fastening buttons or threading a needle or manipulating small objects. (This may result from areas of reduced sensitivity.)

7   Interference with activities Specify which symptoms, and whether interference only occurs in cold weather.

8   Leisure exposure Specify source of exposure and approximate time per week. Do not forget motorcycles. Occasional use of DIY tools is unlikely to be damaging.

9   Alcohol Half a pint of beer = one glass of wine = one measure of spirit = one unit.

10   Medical history A number of conditions are recognised as giving symptoms similar to those of hand-arm vibration syndrome (HAVS). Most of them are rare, and some are listed here:

Vascular

Trauma

Polyarteritis nodosa

Scleroderma

Thoracic outlet syndrome

Toxic effects

Cold haemagglutinins

Systemic lupus erythematosus

Dermatomyositis

Rheumatoid arthritis

Neurological

Trauma to neck or arm

Peripheral nerve entrapment

Peripheral neuropathy

Drug and other toxic effects

CNS disorders   -   Poliomyelitis

                  -   Hemiplegia

Syringomyelia

Spinal cord compression

Multiple sclerosis

11   Leading hand This is applicable to hand-held tools only and is the hand nearer to the source of vibration.

12   Vibration exposure Ask about all activities involving exposure to vibration. A list of tools giving rise to vibration is in paragraph 12 of Chapter 1. Try to estimate the time for which the hands are *actually* exposed to vibration, not just the period during which the tool is used (which is likely to be longer than the actual exposure period). Where work does not follow a regular pattern, an estimate of the range of exposure durations can be given, for example two to three hours per day.

13   Neurotoxic agents and drugs
Possible neurotoxic agents encountered in the workplace include:

n-hexane	methyl butyl ketone
arsenic	carbon disulphide
acrylamide	diethyl thiocarbamate
thallium	mercury compounds
antimony	some organophosphates
TOCP	lead (inorganic)

Rarely, neuropathy may follow the administration of most groups of drugs, for example:

chloramphenicol	isoniazid
streptomycin	polymyxin
ethambutol	nitrofurantoin
metronidazole	gold
indomethacin	vincristine
perhexiline	phenytoin.

14   Room temperature When measured, record value; otherwise record subjective impression as warm/comfortable/cool/cold.

15   Circulation Record blood pressure in both arms. If pulse or blood pressure is reduced in either arm, evidence of a subclavian bruit should be sought.

16   Nervous system A sterile pin or broken orange stick is recommended for eliciting superficial pain. Manual dexterity should be tested using a collection of small coins, washers, bolts or similar objects.

17   Further tests Each of the tests listed in this section of the questionnaire is described in more detail in points (a) to (g):

(a)   *Lewis Prusik test* Pressure is applied to the nail bed for ten seconds and, on release, normal colour should return in two seconds or less. The method is poorly standardised and the result unlikely to be helpful unless it is grossly abnormal.

(b) ***Adson's test*** During deep inspiration, with the head rotated to the side being tested and the arm abducted, the radial artery at the wrist is palpated. In the presence of subclavian obstruction, the radial pulse is reduced or absent. The false positive rate is about ten per cent.

(c) ***Allen's test*** This test examines the patency of the palmar arches and the digital arteries. Normal anatomical variations may give rise to false positive results. The examiner uses the fingers of each hand to compress the radial and ulnar arteries at the wrist and then raises the subject's hand while the subject opens and closes the hand to empty the palmar arches and subcutaneous vessels. The hand is then lowered and one of the arteries released. Prompt flushing of the hand indicates a normal contribution from the tested artery. Faint and delayed flushing of the fingers indicates that either the deep palmar or the digital arteries are occluded. In an established case of HAVS it is said that faint flushing and a delay of more than five seconds indicates digital artery occlusion.

(d) ***Moving two-point discrimination*** Reshape an ordinary paper-clip into two probes which are gently stroked along the surface of the fingertip, ensuring that any barbs are away from the direction of movement. The subject is asked whether he/she can feel one or two points, and the distance between the two points is measured. The procedure is repeated, reducing the distance between the two points until they can no longer be identified as separate. The normal moving two point discrimination at the fingertip has been found to be 2 mm.

(e) ***Tinel's test*** This test and Phalen's test are used to elicit symptoms indicative of carpal tunnel compression. They are both primarily indicated when the subject complains of tingling in the fingers. The subject's hand and forearm are rested horizontally on a flat, firm surface with the palm uppermost. The examiner places his/her index finger over the carpal tunnel at the wrist and applies a sharp tap to it with a tendon hammer. A complaint of tingling in the subject's fingers indicates median nerve compression at the wrist.

(f) ***Phalen's test*** The subject raises his/her arms to chin level and then allows both hands to flex at the wrist by gravity. This posture should be maintained for three minutes. Tingling in the finger is indicative of compression of the median nerve under the carpal ligament.

(g) ***Muscle strength*** This can be tested clinically, against gravity and resistance, or using a dynamometer, when grip strength is most commonly examined. Ensure that the device is zeroed and ask the subject to adopt a standard posture. Usually this will be sitting, with the arm flexed and the forearm supinated and resting on a flat surface. The mean of three successive trials should be recorded.

18   Secondary Raynaud's phenomenon For this diagnosis there should be a history of episodic finger blanching, with no family history and an identified causal factor, whether vibration or a medical condition.

19   Stockholm grading (vascular) Enter the stage and the number of affected digits for each hand.

20   Scoring (vascular) Enter the sum of the scores for each hand separately (see note 3).

21   Stockholm grading (neurological) Enter its stage and number of affected digits for each hand.

22   Latency Record the time between first exposure to vibration and the onset of symptoms.

REFERENCES
AND
FURTHER READING

REFERENCES

1 *A Guide to the Reporting of Injuries, Diseases and Dangerous Occurrences Regulations 1985* HS(R)23 HSE 1986 ISBN 0 7176 0432 2

2 *Management of Health and Safety at Work Regulations 1992: Approved Code of Practice* L21 HSE 1992 ISBN 0 7176 0412 8

3 British Standards Institution BS 6842:1987 *Guide to measurements and evaluation of human exposure to vibration transmitted to the hand*

4 International Standards Organisation ISO 5349:1989 *Mechanical vibration guidelines for the measurement and the assessment of human exposure to hand-transmitted vibration*

5 Taylor W and Pelmear P L (Editors) *Vibration white finger in industry* Academic Press 1975 ISBN 0 12 684550 6

6 British Standards Institution BS 7482:1991 *Instrumentation for the measurement of vibration exposure to human beings:*
Part 1: *Specification for general requirements for instrumentation for measuring the vibration applied to human beings*
Part 2: *Specification for instrumentation for measuring vibration transmitted to the hand*

7 International Standards Organisation ISO 8041:1990 *Human response to vibration-measuring instrumentation*

8 Carlson W S, Samueloff S and others. Instrumentation for the measurement of sensory loss in fingertips, *J Occup Med* 1976, **21**, 260-264

FURTHER READING

Brammer A J, Taylor W and others. Sensorineural stages of the hand-arm vibration syndrome *Scandinavian Journal of Work, Environment and Health* 1987 **13**(4), 279-283

Faculty of Occupational Medicine of the Royal College of Physicians *Hand-transmitted vibration: clinical effects and pathophysiology. Part 1: Report of a working party* The Royal College of Physicians 1993 ISBN 1 873240 51 1

Gemne G, Pyykkoe I and others. The Stockholm Workshop scale for the classification of cold-induced Raynaud's phenomenon in the hand-arm vibration syndrome (revision of the Taylor Pelmear scale), *Scandinavian Journal of Work, Environment and Health* 1987 **13**(4), 275-6

Griffin M J *The effects of vibration on health* (ISVR Memorandum 632) Institute of Sound and Vibration, University of Southampton 1982

Griffin M J *Handbook of human vibration* Academic Press 1990 ISBN 0 12 303040 4

HSE *Hand-arm vibration: advice for employers* Free leaflet IND(G)175(L) HSE 1994

HSE *Hand-arm vibration: advice on vibration white finger for employees and the self-employed* Free leaflet IND(G)126(L) HSE 1994

HSE *Survey of exposure to hand-arm vibration in Great Britain* Research Paper No 26: manufacturing, public utilities, construction, agriculture and forestry HSE 1988 ISBN 0 11 885932 3 Research Paper No 29: mines and quarries HSE 1991 ISBN 0 11 885900 5

HSE *Surveillance of people exposed to health risks at work* HS(G)61 HSE 1990 ISBN 0 11 885574 3

Pelmear P L, Taylor W and others (Editors) *Hand-arm vibration. A comprehensive guide for occupational health professionals* Van Nostrand Reinhold (New York) 1992 ISBN 0 44 201250 0

Printed and published by the Health and Safety Executive   C100   6/94

64